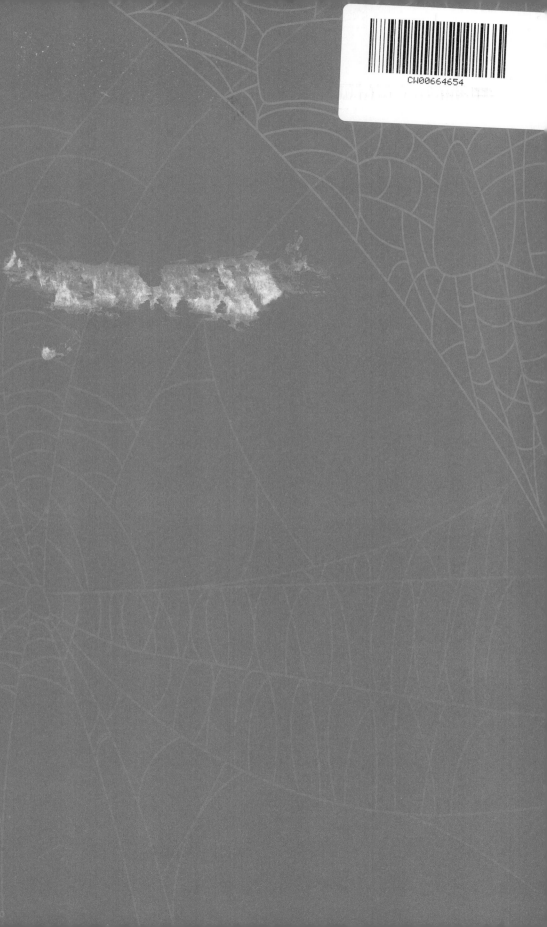

# ILLUSTRATED GUIDE TO THE
# SPIDER-VERSE

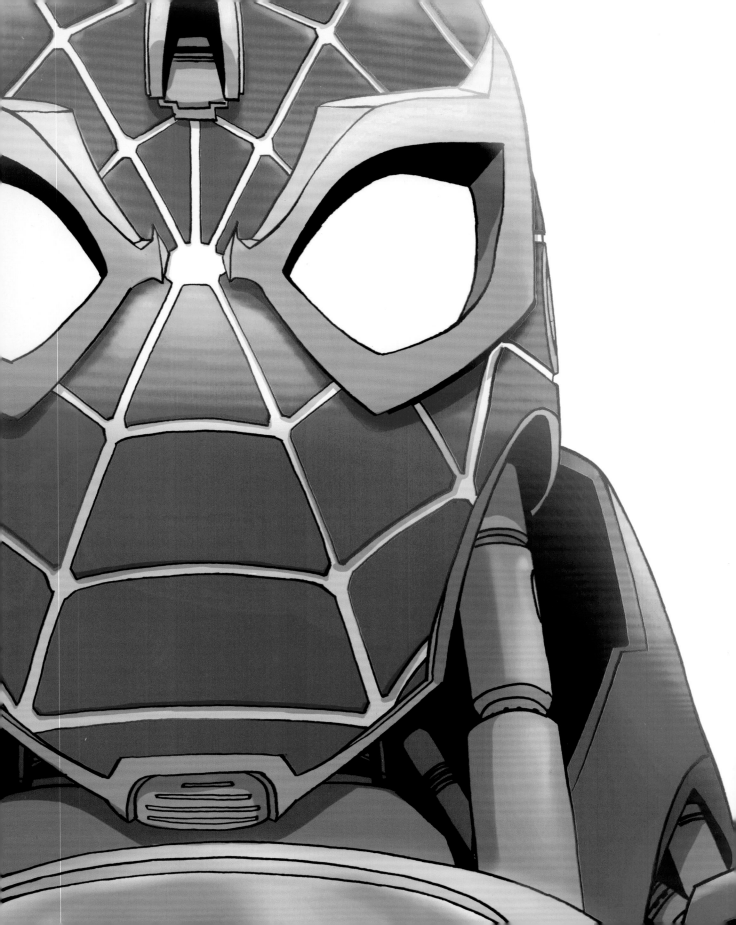

# ILLUSTRATED GUIDE TO THE
# SPIDER-VERSE

Written by

## MARC SUMERAK

Illustrated by

## GIUSEPPE CAMUNCOLI

## YANCEY LABAT

## MARCO DEL FORNO

TITAN
BOOKS

*London*

# INTRODUCTION

## "What is a family?"

That's the question my history professor at Empire State University wants us to answer for our first assignment in this semester's genealogy unit. And, on the surface, it seems like a pretty simple question. I mean, no matter who we are or where we come from—whether we're normal kids or web-swinging wonders—family is the one thing we all have in common, right?

But that doesn't mean all families are the same. Not even close. Family comes in all kinds of forms: Some big, some small. Some traditional, some unconventional. Some close, some estranged. Some present, some long gone.

Until recently, my family was just me and my dad—Gwen Stacy and Captain George Stacy of the NYPD. After Mom died, Dad did the best he could, trying to raise an overly rebellious teenage daughter while protecting the city from an end-less supply of criminals and crazies. He may not always have thought I was paying attention to what he was trying to teach me, but the example he set made him more than just my father—it made him my hero. And it made me want to be just like him. Turns out, I'd get my chance sooner than I ever expected.

One little bite from a radioactive spider, and *boom!*—I'm a real-life super-hero. No, I'm serious! I went from laying down sick beats with my band, the Mary Janes, to beating down super-villains as the spectacular Spider-Woman. Obviously, I tried to live up to what my dad taught me and do the right thing—you know, use my powers responsi-bly to help people and stuff? But then one of my close friends died—and I got the blame. (Actually, my wall-crawling alter ego did. No one knew it was me—yet.) I went from being NYC's hottest new hero

to Public Enemy No. 1 overnight. For Pete's sake, my own father was trying to hunt me down and bring me to justice! I'd never felt so alone in my whole life.

But when things looked the darkest for your friendly neighborhood Spider-Gwen, that's when I learned an important lesson: Family isn't just the people we're bound to by blood. It can also be the people we're bound to by purpose. And before I knew it, my family suddenly became a whole lot bigger than I could have possibly imagined. (Stay with me—this is where things get weird. Well, weird*er*.)

Believe it or not, the world we live in is just one of an infinite number of realities. A simple change to a single moment is all it takes for a separate timeline to diverge and spin off in an entirely different direction. Results may vary, of course, which means some alternate Earths seem strangely familiar, while others are barely recog-nizable. But no matter how much things diverge, these universes are still tied together by common threads—kinda like a giant web of what could be. And who better to protect a web than a spider? Lucky for the Multiverse, there are plenty of us to go around!

Like I said, each reality, no matter how different, shares some constants. One of those is the pres-ence of a spiderific hero like me. Apparently, I'm just one of many Spider-Totems—superpowered beings with an unusually strong connection to the so-called Web of Life and Destiny. No matter which dimension you call home, you're bound to find one of us swinging around somewhere.

Most of us share the same basic powers: enhanced strength, durability, and agility; the ability to adhere to most surfaces; and a sort of sixth sense that gives us a heads-up when danger is coming—the standard spider stuff. But while our superhuman skill sets may be similar, we've all got our own unique personalities and stories that set us apart. Take away our masks, and it's clear that no two Spider-Heroes are exactly alike. (Unless they're clones, maybe—but even then . . .)

Normally, we tend to stick to our home multiversal neighborhoods, protecting our own worlds in our own ways. But there have been times when we've had to cross the boundaries between dimensions and form our own little Spider-Armies in order to save everything that is. Whenever we've come together, it's been clear to me that the deep bonds we Spider-types share make us so much more than just another team of super-heroes. We laugh, we cry, we fight, we make up, and we drive each other totally nuts—but we're always there for each other when it counts the most, no matter what. (Well, most of us, at least.) If that isn't a family, I don't know what is.

Since I first donned the webs, I've been back and forth between realities more times than I can count, and I've had the honor of getting to know many of my brothers- and sisters-in-arms along the way. But while we may have shared an instant connection, there's still a lot to learn about each of my cross-dimensional counterparts. Plus, there are tons of Spideys out there that I haven't even had the chance to team up with yet. So, in the spirit of my history assignment, I'm going to take a closer look at my amazing new family in an effort to better understand who they all are—and, hopefully, how I fit in.

Will I be able to turn this in for a grade? No way! Not without completely giving away my secret identity and having to transfer to another school (or another universe). But that doesn't make the work I'm doing here any less valuable. Because when my family has a reunion, it usually means that the end of the world is closing in on us—and that's exactly when I need to know who is watching my back and fighting by my side.

So, grab some snacks and crank up the tunes, kids, 'cause this is one study session that I can guarantee you won't want to skip. We're about to dive face-first into the Spider-Verse!

—Gwen

PS—If you're reading this, it means that I trust you to keep all of these details on the down-low. Why? First off, the concept of the Multiverse alone is enough to make most normal peoples' heads explode. But even more importantly, there's a lot of top-secret info about my amazing Spidey-friends in here that could cause them some huge headaches if it got into the wrong hands. Do you want to be the reason a gang of interdimensional Goblins starts hunting them down? Didn't think so. So, keep a lid on it, yeah?

PPS—Naturally, almost every Spider-Hero believes that they're the real deal, and their chosen super-hero names usually reflect that fact. But if I just call everyone Spider-Man here, things are gonna get confusing real fast. So in a few cases, I've added little nicknames that I use to help me tell them all apart. Do me a favor, though, and try not to call them by those names if you meet them in person (especially "Spider-Punk"!). These are for easy identification purposes only—got it?

# SPIDER-MAN

You can't really talk about Spider-Heroes without talking about my pal Peter Parker, the sensational Spider-Man. That's because in, like, 90 percent of realities, Pete was the one chosen to wear the webs. And of all the Peter Parkers on all the alternate Earths, none of them have swung to the same epic heights as the Pete who hails from the dimension that I now call home—Reality-616.

(REALITY-616)

To be fair, his story is a pretty familiar one. Bitten by an irradiated spider during a science experiment gone wrong, the teenage Pete gained a bunch of uncanny abilities. His natural speed, strength, and agility were boosted way beyond the levels of a normal human, he can cling to walls, and he can sense imminent danger. So, on that front, he and I really aren't all that different.

But one gift that Pete possessed even before he became an arachnid avatar was his genius-level intellect. He used his scientific know-how to design his signature web-shooters, as well as the synthetic polymer "webbing" that they project. He uses that stuff to swing through the city, bind his enemies, and weave a slew of useful tools for hero-ing. And he was still in high school when he came up with the formula! I know—crazy, right?

It's not just Pete's powers or smarts that define him as a hero, though. He's also got a noble spirit, an unwavering moral compass, and a deeply ingrained sense of responsibility, all of which have helped him beat the odds over and over again. He knows from firsthand experience that if the kind of power we have isn't used wisely, the consequences can be totally disastrous—and, to him, that's simply not an option.

That's why, as Spider-Man, Pete continues to step up and face off against even the most impossible challenges, always putting the safety of innocent people before his own personal well-being. He may have started his crime-fighting career on a relatively small scale, keeping the streets of his neighborhood safe, but since then, this Spidey has gone on to save his world—and even the Multiverse itself—on more occasions than he'd ever willingly admit.

Believe me, I've met my fair share of Spideys from across the dimensions, but there's no doubt in my mind as to why this particular Spider-Man has earned his spot at the center of the web.

# GHOST-SPIDER

## (REALITY-65)

Look, this whole thing really isn't supposed to be about me. There are so many other Spider-Heroes out there with way cooler stories than mine to explore. Still, in case you're interested, I guess I could share a few more fun facts about myself— the stunningly spectacular Ghost-Spider:

- I live in Reality-616 these days, but I'm originally from Reality-65. On my Earth, I was the one who got the big bite and all the cool powers that came along with it. I became Spider-Woman, while the Peter Parker from my world—he wasn't quite so lucky.

- Remember when I said that everyone on my Earth blamed me for someone's death? Yeah—that was Pete. He'd always been bullied, and he thought superpowers like mine might be the ticket to breaking that cycle. So he decided to experiment on himself. It didn't go well. He transformed into this lizardlike monster and attacked our school, forcing me to fight back. I didn't know it was him until it was too late.

- Anyway—what else? Oh! I eventually lost my spider-powers but managed to regain almost identical abilities by bonding with an alien symbiote. (It's honestly not as creepy as it sounds.)

- Like most Spideys, I wear web-shooters. But mine were invented by my world's version of Janet Van Dyne, who you probably know as the Wasp. I also got hooked up with a cool interdimensional transporter device. It may look like a high-tech wristwatch, but it allows me to cross over into other realities in the blink of an eye. A bunch of us Web-Warriors had them for a while, but mine's one of the few that still works.

- OK, back to the heavy stuff for a sec. After Pete died, I went on the run for a while, gaining bona fide vigilante status while still trying my best to earn some redemption. I eventually came to terms with the fact that I was doing more harm than good, though, so I surrendered and spent a year in prison to atone for my reckless behavior. It wasn't the best experience, but it earned me back a lot of the respect I had lost—especially from my dad.

- Even though I made up for my mistakes, things back in Reality-65 got . . . complicated. So, I decided to come here, to an Earth where my identity is still a secret and my life isn't a hot mess. Now, I get to start fresh. New dimension. New code name. And a new chapter in my heroic career!

    *Aaaaaand* I think that pretty much covers it! Now, let's shift the focus to someone who's *really* out of this world.

# SPIDER-MAN

## (REALITY-13) "COSMIC SPIDER-MAN"

Out in the cosmos, there's this insanely powerful concentration of sentient celestial energy that embodies life, light, and creation. We call it the Enigma Force. Sometimes, a portion of this ancient entity (known as the Uni-Power) forms bonds with organic beings, granting them access to its nearly unlimited cosmic awesomeness.

The Enigma Force is said to be pretty selective of its hosts, choosing only the most virtuous people to wield its godlike might and become Captain Universe. So, it's no big surprise that Peter Parkers from a bunch of realities have been chosen as its champions. Most Spider-Heroes have voluntarily relinquished its unimaginable powers—which include cosmically heightened senses, flight, and matter manipulation—once whatever crisis they were facing had been averted.

But the Peter Parker of Reality-13 held on to the Uni-Power, boosting his already impressive abilities in the war against eternal darkness—until he died saving his fellow Spiders from certain doom. The Enigma Force may have made him one with his universe, but I hope he had the chance to see how much better he made all of ours.

# SPIDER-MAN

## (REALITY-138)

## "SPIDER-PUNK"

Most Spider-Heroes fight to uphold the law, but the Spider-Man from Reality-138? Not so much. See, my friend Hobie Brown came from a world where an authoritarian regime was crushing its lowest classes and pretending it was patriotism. When Hobie got bitten by a spider that was irradiated due to illegal toxic dumping, he used his newfound abilities to fight the powers that be. Passionate and free spirited, Hobie relies on his sharp tongue and loud guitar to amplify his crusade against inequality—but in the face of fascists, he's more than happy to let his fists do the talking! Brown formed his own personal Spider-Army of freedom fighters to topple the status quo on his world.

After that, he joined an entirely different kind of Spider-Army—one composed of his fellow Spider-Heroes from multiple realities—to save the Multiverse. I'm always glad to jam with this dude any chance we get, because when we're together, one thing's for sure—the hits won't stop coming!

# MAN-SPIDER

## (REALITY-666)

Wanna hear something really gross? In a handful of realities, Spider-Man's arachnidlike characteristics were magnified to the point where he became, well, more spider than man. With additional limbs, multiple eyes, and deadly, venomous fangs, his physical appearance became the stuff of nightmares. (Seriously. It's not a great look.)

Fortunately, in most instances, these beastly transformations have only been temporary, brought about by exposure to strange technologies, mutagenic substances, or some other form of bad mojo. However, in some dimensions, like Reality-666—where Earth was dominated by supernatural forces—the resident Spider-Man ended up retaining these hideous features permanently. Call me an optimist, but even when a Spidey's more savage side comes to the surface, I like to believe that he still has the heart of a hero—somewhere within that grotesquely mutated thorax.

# SP//dr

Of all the various Spider-Heroes I've had the pleasure of teaming up with over the years, few have had the same level of cool as Peni Parker. (No offense, boys, but you know it's true.) Peni inherited a high-tech mechanized suit of armor known as the SP//dr after the death of her father, the suit's original pilot.

In order to operate the SP//dr, Peni had to allow herself to be bitten by the sentient radioactive spider that lives inside the suit's CPU. The bite forged a psychic connection between Peni and the armor, giving her full access to its massive assortment of functions. Using the SP//dr's enhanced strength, durability, and web-based weaponry, Peni devoted herself to her father's mission of keeping the Earth in Reality-14512 safe from a variety of threats. But even though she's suffered a number of personal tragedies since she first suited up, Peni hasn't hesitated when called into action alongside her fellow Spider-Heroes. I couldn't be happier knowing she and SP//dr are on my team.

# SPIDER-WOMAN

## (REALITY-616)

When I started my crime-fighting career back in Reality-65, I originally used the name Spider-Woman. But when I decided to relocate here to Reality-616, I knew that name was already taken. I suppose I could have fought for the title, but I already had way too much respect for the woman who held it. Honestly, I can't think of anyone more deserving to be this dimension's official Spider-Woman than my girl Jessica Drew.

Unlike most of us who gained our powers from spider bites, Jess was subjected to unorthodox experiments from an early age. Her own father injected her with a serum derived from the blood of spiders, in hopes that its regenerative properties might cure Jess of an illness she had contracted. The poor kid was sealed inside of a healing chamber for years until the serum took full effect. When she finally emerged, she was fully grown and had an unexpected array of sweet new abilities.

Spider-Woman's powers span a much wider range than the average Spider-Hero. Jess can release powerful bioelectric blasts from her hands that can stun her foes. She's also been able to generate pheromones that allow her to influence the emotions of those around her. She even has a healing factor that makes her immune to toxins and slows her aging process. When added to more standard spider-based abilities she has, like wall-crawling and enhanced strength, speed, and reflexes, it's pretty clear why this Spider-Woman stands apart from her fellow Web-Warriors.

Over the years, Jess has pushed the boundaries of what it means to be a super-hero. She's walked so many paths, proving herself as an agent of both S.H.I.E.L.D. and S.W.O.R.D., as well as being a bounty hunter, a private detective, and a devoted mother. And since it looks like her adorable little son, Gerry, has inherited many of his mom's sensational gifts, I think it's fair to say that this Spider-Woman's adventures have only just begun!

# SPIDER-UK

## (REALITY-833)

Long before we ever gathered our own Spider-Army to save the Multiverse, there were plenty of other groups already taking point when it came to ensuring the safety of all realities. One of them is the Corps, an assemblage of omniversal protectors with representatives in virtually every known universe. Most Corps members are variations of Captain Britain, but one of them, Billy Braddock of Reality-833, also happened to be his world's version of Spider-Man. Pretty cool, right? Gifted with a talisman that let him travel between dimensions, Billy was the key to bringing all of us Spideys together for the very first time in order to fight a ruthless family of totem hunters known as the Inheritors.

When the fight was finished, the Spider-Heroes got the win—but poor Billy lost more than he ever could have anticipated. His own reality, which he had sworn to protect, had fallen victim to another catastrophe in his absence. Still, he managed to find new purpose, devoting himself to helping his fellow Spider-Heroes from across the Web of Life and Destiny until he eventually fell in battle fighting at our side. There may be millions of Spideys out there in the Multiverse, but we'll never find another one quite like him.

# SPIDER-KID

## [REALITY-218]

In the vast majority of realities, Peter Parker will gladly regale you with long-winded stories about how he learned the importance of using his powers responsibly thanks to the guidance of his beloved Uncle Ben. But it turns out that not all Ben Parkers inspire heroism—particularly the one from Reality-218. After enduring years of abuse at his uncle's hands, that dimension's young Peter Parker chose to run away. Spending his formative years in group homes and juvenile detention centers, he even changed his name to Charlie to further distance himself from his family.

But the one thing he couldn't distance himself from was his destiny. Like his counterparts on so many other worlds, Charlie gained spider-powers, which he now uses to combat drug dealers and keep the streets of his neighborhood safe. Although some of his choices might be considered, let's say, less than heroic, the kid's still learning. With the right guidance from his fellow Spiders, there's still plenty of time for him to grow into the hero he was meant to be.

# DOPPELGANGER

## (REALITY-616)

OK—get this: Pete told me that there was some massive cosmic confrontation a while back where a villain known as the Magus created twisted replicas of Reality-616's most powerful heroes and let them loose on the world. When the battle ended, all of the devious duplicates were destroyed—except for one. Want to take a guess at whose evil twin made it out alive? Yep! You got it! It seems Spider-Man's dupe had formed a mystical bond with a third-rate villain known as Demogoblin, somehow saving him from the fate of his fiendish friends.

And apparently, he's still out there somewhere. Which is not great, because beyond his funhouse-mirror physiology—which includes extra appendages and razor-sharp teeth and talons—this creepy copy also possesses most of the same enhanced powers as Spidey himself. Even worse, Pete's intelligence and sense of responsibility weren't replicated, making the deranged Doppelganger a real danger to anyone unfortunate enough to end up trapped in his web.

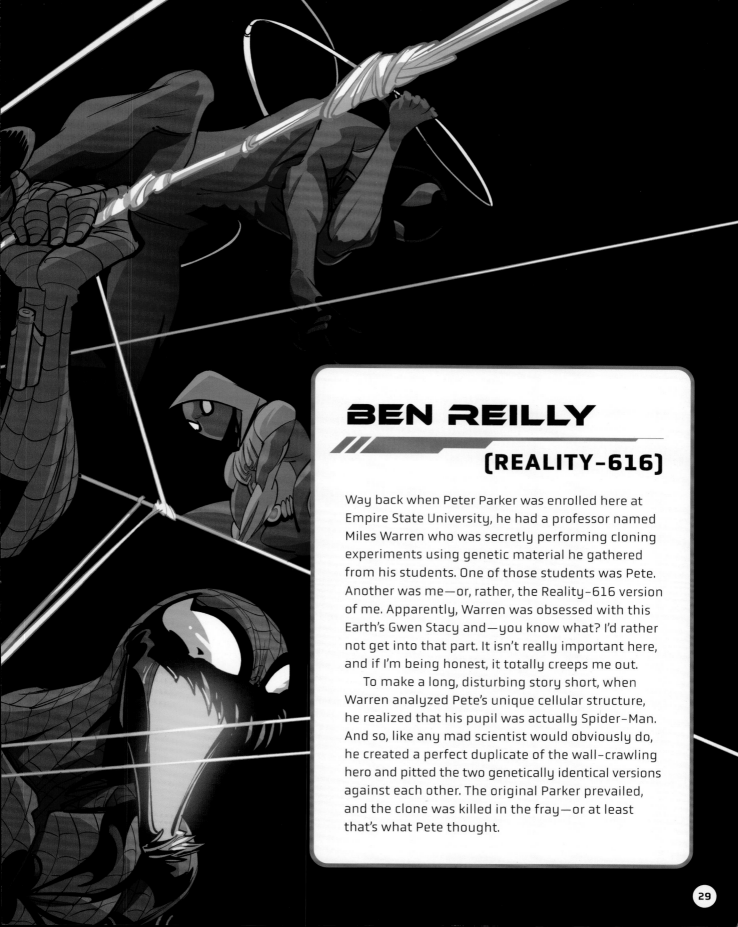

# BEN REILLY

## (REALITY-616)

Way back when Peter Parker was enrolled here at Empire State University, he had a professor named Miles Warren who was secretly performing cloning experiments using genetic material he gathered from his students. One of those students was Pete. Another was me—or, rather, the Reality-616 version of me. Apparently, Warren was obsessed with this Earth's Gwen Stacy and—you know what? I'd rather not get into that part. It isn't really important here, and if I'm being honest, it totally creeps me out.

To make a long, disturbing story short, when Warren analyzed Pete's unique cellular structure, he realized that his pupil was actually Spider-Man. And so, like any mad scientist would obviously do, he created a perfect duplicate of the wall-crawling hero and pitted the two genetically identical versions against each other. The original Parker prevailed, and the clone was killed in the fray—or at least that's what Pete thought.

The truth is, the clone managed to survive the encounter. But when he realized that he wasn't the genuine article (despite sharing Pete's memories, personality, and powers), he went into self-imposed exile. He took on a new name, Ben Reilly—a tribute to his beloved Uncle Ben and Aunt May (whose maiden name was Reilly)—and attempted to make a new life for himself far from the New York City streets that the real Peter Parker protected.

But escaping the web of Spider-Man is no easy feat, and since then, Ben has been drawn back into Pete's life on a number of occasions—sometimes as a friend, other times not so much. He's worn a bunch of different masks over the years, even taking over as the official Spider-Man of Reality-616 every now and then when Pete wasn't available to don the webs. But the identity that Ben returns to the most is one that he forged himself: the Scarlet Spider. Despite us not always seeing eye to eye, any Spidey who can rock a vintage hoodie in battle automatically gets a few extra points on my list.

While he may seem physically identical to the original Peter Parker in every way, Ben's cloned genetic structure has proven to be unstable and has broken down on multiple occasions. If what Ben says is true, he actually has died and been reborn in new cloned bodies close to thirty times now! It's a vicious cycle that has obviously caused some long-lasting effects on his state of mind.

Having inherited Pete's indomitable spirit, Ben Reilly has always found ways to keep fighting on, even in the face of death. But the more trauma he's experienced, the wider the chasm has grown between the man Ben was created to mirror and the one he has ultimately become. And, as far as I can tell, that's not a good thing . . . for any of us . . .

# SCARLET SPIDERS

## (REALITY-616)

Though it may be hard to believe, not all of the Spider-Heroes out there possess spider-based powers. For example, there's the Scarlet Spiders from right here in Reality-616— a team of three identical heroes who once served as part of a program called the Avengers Initiative.

Just like the original Scarlet Spider, Ben Reilly, these guys were clones. But in this case, it wasn't Peter Parker who was their original genetic template. Instead, they were derived from the DNA of some kid named

Michael Van Patrick, a young hero whose body was considered to be the perfect specimen of peak human ability. When Van Patrick was killed in action, three clones of him (named Michael, Van, and Patrick, of course) were secretly created and given suits of Iron Spider armor—liquid-metal nanofiber suits originally developed by Tony Stark—to enhance their natural skills. Sadly, two of the three Scarlet Spiders followed their "father" to an early grave, but Patrick survived to keep fighting in honor of his fallen brothers.

# SPIDER-WOMAN

## (REALITY-807128)

There may be fewer Spider-Women than Spider-Men in the Multiverse, but what we lack in numbers, we more than make up for in attitude—and Ashley Barton is the perfect example of that. Born into the dystopian future of Reality-807128, she didn't have a close relationship with her father, Clint Barton, the former Avenger known as Hawkeye. She instead took after her mother, Tonya, who happened to be the daughter of that Earth's Peter Parker.

Utilizing the spider-powers that had been passed down to her across generations, Ashley assembled a group of heroes to retake control of the city of Hammer Falls (Las Vegas to you and me) from the ruthless Kingpin. While her teammates didn't survive the encounter, Ashley managed to escape execution with the help of her estranged father. But much to her father's dismay, she then killed the Kingpin and took his spot as the new ruler of Hammer Falls! Luckily, she has taken a slightly more heroic turn since then, aiding her fellow Spider-Heroes in our fight against multiversal threats. As far as I can tell, I'm on her good side for now—and I plan to do whatever it takes to stay there, just to be safe.

# LADY SPIDER

## (REALITY-803)

Speaking of ladies with attitude, meet Maybelle Reilly of Reality-803. She may not have been bitten by a spider and imbued with spectacular powers like me, but an arachnid encounter did inspire her to become a hero. Maybelle used her amazing intellect and cutting-edge mechanical skills to build a powerful four-legged harness capable of scaling walls, using only technology equivalent to what would have been available in our late nineteenth century. She also designed and built her own web-shooters, which she uses to fight crime under the guise of Lady Spider (which sounds super-classy!).

Although Maybelle's Earth isn't nearly as technologically advanced as most others in the Multiverse, her inventions have allowed her to hold her own against formidable foes such as the Six Men of Sinestry (another name that's pretty fancy!). This steampunk Spidey has shown that she's willing to fight for her world—and all others—with a spirit that cannot be caged!

# EZEKIEL SIMS

## (REALITY-616)

Years before Peter Parker was bitten by a radioactive spider, another resident of Reality-616 underwent an ancient ritual to gain spider-powers of his own. This guy, named Ezekiel Sims, could have used the spiderlike skills he acquired to become a hero like the rest of us—but, instead, he focused on amassing a fortune and securing his legacy. Not cool. He kept to the shadows for a long time, until a being named Morlun began hunting for spider-powered prey in Reality-616.

That's when Ezekiel finally revealed his existence to Spider-Man and joined the fight.

Though Ezekiel passed along a great deal of knowledge about the nature of spider-powers to his new protégé, he was also desperate to cling to his own abilities. Ezekiel nearly sacrificed Pete to a mystic entity known as the Gatekeeper in order to retain his powers. Fortunately, he had a last-minute change of heart, giving his own life so that the more heroic Spider-Man could fight another day.

# OLD MAN SPIDER

## (REALITY-4)

The Ezekiel Sims of Reality-616 may have been able to save this world's Spider-Man from death at the hands of Morlun, but that wasn't the case in Reality-4. On that Earth, Peter Parker fell victim to the vicious spider hunter, leaving Sims to take up the mantle and legacy of Spider-Man himself.

I actually got to meet this slightly more-heroic version of Ezekiel the first time our Spider-Army assembled to fight against Morlun's family, the Inheritors. He was a bit gruff, sure, but he seemed like a decent enough guy. Unfortunately, all the secret stuff he knew about the Inheritors made him a prime target. He ended up as one of the first casualties in the confrontation, but the critical info he dropped on us between his dying breaths eventually helped us win the war against his greatest foes. It's just a shame he didn't live long enough to celebrate the victory with us.

# SPIDER-MAN

Wait—how have I gotten this far without talking about Miles Morales?! Peter Parker may have set the bar for what a Spider-Man is supposed to be, but when my boy Miles swung in, his style and flair took the game to a whole new level!

When I first met Miles, he was the resident Spider-Man of Reality-1610. But he wasn't the first one to wear the webs on his world. That Earth's original Spidey was—surprise!—yet another Peter Parker. When that Pete was struck down in a battle against the Green Goblin, the world mourned the loss of their beloved hero. But it wouldn't be long before a brand-new Spider-Man stepped up to fill the void that Pete left behind.

See, in Reality-1610, the spider that bit Peter Parker was merely one subject in a series of experiments involving a top secret formula created by Oscorp—a super-sketchy company run by the Green Goblin himself, Norman Osborn. A different spider exposed to a variation of the same serum found its way out of the Oscorp lab and ended up biting yet another brilliant young student. (I guess the spiders on that world had very specific tastes.)

The enhanced spider's bite gave Miles abilities similar to those of his predecessor, but also a bunch of bonus powers that the previous Spider-Man of his world didn't possess. Those include a bioelectric sting, which Miles refers to as a Venom Blast, and a natural camouflage ability that essentially allows him to become invisible to the naked eye. (Hmm—maybe *he* should have gone with "Ghost-Spider.")

Although Miles did his very best to protect his home dimension as its new Spider-Man, Reality-1610 eventually became one of many casualties in some kind of secret cosmic war that nearly decimated the Multiverse. From what I understand, Miles somehow managed to step up and prove himself when all of existence was on the line (which, if you've met Miles, totally tracks). So, when the war was over, Miles and the people he loved most were granted a new chance at life here in Reality-616.

Now Miles is finally able to swing through the streets of New York City alongside Peter Parker, the same hero whose webs he once tried to fill. But while he may be grateful to have another shot at living up to his idol's legacy, he's also determined to forge his own path as the next generation's Spider-Man. As much as I love the O.G. Spidey, I've gotta admit, Miles Morales is the ultimate Spidey in my book!

# BLACK WIDOW

## (REALITY-1610)

Miles Morales may have been the successor to the Spider-Man of Reality-1610, but he wasn't the only hero to carry on the legacy of that dimension's Peter Parker. From what Miles has told me, the Spider-Woman from his home world turned out to be from a group of modified Peter Parker clones that were created to work as super-powered agents for the government. She and her fellow clones managed to escape from the program that spawned them, eventually cross-ing paths with the real Pete. This clone—who chose to go by the name Jessica Drew—was nearly identical to her progenitor in terms of memories and powers. But beyond the obvious gender differences, she also had a unique ability to produce an organic form of webbing from her fingertips. When the Peter Parker of Reality-1610 was tragically killed, his clone had every right to decide who got to inherit his mantle. She made a solid choice, giving Miles her blessing to officially claim the name of Spider-Man (eventually) while she continued to fight the good fight, first as Spider-Woman and then as Black Widow.

# SPIDERCIDE

## (REALITY-616)

Remember that skeezy jerk Miles Warren that I told you about? The guy with the clone obsession? Like I said before, his first clone of Spider-Man—the one who went on to be known as Ben Reilly—was designed to be an identical copy of Peter Parker. Unfortunately, Warren's experimentation didn't end there. He continued to fine-tune his cloning process, creating a number of Parker duplicates over the years.

One of them was supposed to represent what Spider-Man might become after 10,000 years of evolution. This clone developed the ability to manipulate his body mass on a molecular level, allowing him to change his size, shape, and appearance. Convinced that he was the one true Peter Parker, this clone devoted himself to striking down anyone who kept him from reclaiming the life he felt he was owed. Eventually, when he learned the truth about his origins, he took the name Spidercide and went on a killing spree. After being mortally wounded during a fall, his remains were put into stasis, hopefully never to be released upon this world (or any other) ever again.

# THE SPIDER

## (REALITY-311)

Depending on which dimension you're in, time can get kinda wonky. For instance, over in Reality-311, their Earth's present day is, like, four hundred years in our past. In their year 1602, a young Peter Parquagh served as the assistant of Sir Nicholas Fury. Fury made himself an enemy of the new king of England when he refused to kill superhumans—known as the witchbreed on their world. So, Parquagh was captured by the king and sent across the sea to the colony of Roanoke, where he was ordered to kill his mentor. Parquagh wouldn't go through with that mission, and decided instead to make a fresh start in the New World.

While he was there, Parquagh was bitten by a spider that had been infused with strange temporal energies. Gaining superhuman abilities and becoming a witchbreed himself, he performed selfless acts of heroism in the guise of the Spider. Parquagh eventually returned to England, taking his final bow on the stage of the Globe Theatre when he was struck down by Morlun in the opening act of our war against the Inheritors.

# PRINCE OF ARACHNE

To folks without powers, being a super-hero probably seems like some kind of fairy tale. In the case of the Peter Parker from Reality-71004, that sentiment couldn't be truer. This guy's origin was a literal Cinderella story—well, at least for the first few chapters.

After he was orphaned, Peter was taken in by Norman and Harry Osborn, who treated him like a mere servant. Peter wanted to go to some fancy royal ball to win the chance to marry Princess Gwendolyn (who I'm assuming was super-cute and totally worth the hassle). Since his new family wouldn't allow it, Peter disguised himself in a suit of fancy spider-themed armor he built. He managed to win Gwen's heart as the mysterious Prince of Arachne, but she ended up getting killed before they could get their happily ever after (which seems to happen way too often for my taste). Sadly, Sir Peter would soon share the same fate as his beloved when the Inheritors attacked and cut his story far too short.

# WEB-SLINGER & WIDOW

## (REALITY-31913)

Ever wonder what Spider-Man might've been like if he'd been born in the rugged deserts of the American Southwest instead of the steel canyons of New York City? Well, wonder no more! Over in Reality-31913, Patrick O'Hara earned his reputation as an expert gunslinger long before he gained any sort of superhuman powers. But when a spider was accidentally bathed in an enchanted elixir, its bite transferred enhanced abilities not only to O'Hara but also to his horse, Widow. Yeah, you heard me right—dude's got a Spider-Horse!

Linked by a psychic connection, the pair began to ride down a new path together—one that led toward justice. Donning an all-too-familiar mask and the alias Ponderosa Parker, O'Hara devoted his powers and pistols to stopping the worst villains in the West. Yee-haw! But though he may share many of the same powers as his fellow Spider-Heroes, O'Hara doesn't always share our moral code. This Web-Slinger has no qualms putting a bullet between the eyes of any varmint who he feels deserves it. Yee-ikes!

# SPIDER-GIRL

## (REALITY-616)

Anya Corazon was just a regular teenager from Reality-616 until she got mixed up with an ancient cult known as the Spider Society. The secret sect drafted her to become their newest Hunter—one in a long line of spider-powered warriors that stretches back for centuries. Calling herself Araña, she used her newly unlocked abilities to fight against the society's sworn enemies, the Sisterhood of the Wasp.

Anya eventually learned that she wasn't truly destined to be a Hunter and left the Spider Society behind, but she kept on doing the hero thing. She inherited a new costume from a former Spider-Woman named Julia Carpenter (more on her later!) and decided to officially adopt the code name Spider-Girl—since everyone was already calling her that anyway. Like me, Anya lost her powers for a while, but she got them back when this weird thing happened where pretty much everybody in Manhattan gained spiderlike abilities for a hot second. Luckily, she managed to hang on to hers even after the rest of the island was cured.

Anya and I first teamed up during that whole multiversal mess with the Inheritors that I mentioned earlier. Her ability to read the ancient totemic runes of the Spider Society made a huge difference when it came to pulling out a big win for Team Spidey. After that, we kept hanging out as members of a cross-dimensional Spider-squad, protecting the Web of Life and Destiny. And then we both went on to be founding members of the Order of the Web, a collective of Spider-Heroes based here in the 616. In our time together, Anya has proven to be not only a true hero but also an amazing Spider-friend!

# SAVAGE SPIDER-MAN

## (REALITY-83043)

If you think that one spider bite sounds like too much, you're not gonna believe what the Peter Parker from Reality-83043 had to go through to get his powers! After his family's plane went down in Antarctica, a very young Pete was found by a species of massive spiders dwelling in the bizarre prehistoric refuge known as the Savage Land. He told me that he was subjected to something called the Trial of 1,000 Venoms, which is somehow even worse than it sounds. Basically, the giant spiders would bite him over and over, only giving him enough time to heal before repeating the process.

The poison in his veins eventually made him stronger and enhanced his senses, and the spiders accepted him as part of their clutter. This Spider-Man then became the new protector of the Savage Land until total Spider-Geddon broke out in the Multiverse. That's when I recruited him to take his hunt to a whole new dimension!

# SPIDER-MAN (REALITY-92100)

## "SIX-ARMED SPIDER-MAN"

Looking for a Spider-Man who's a bit more spidery than most, but maybe without all of the creepy extra eyes and pointy, venomous fangs? Then you probably would have dug the Peter Parker from Reality-92100. While trying to cure himself of his spider-powers, he took a serum that ended up doing exactly the opposite, giving him four extra arms (for a total of eight appendages, just like your average arachnid). The Peter Parker from here in Reality-616 told me that the same thing happened to him once, but he managed to find a cure (which kinda sucks, 'cause it's a rad look!).

Anyway, this Spidey saw his legion of limbs as a curse at first too, but he eventually learned that having a few extra hands in battle wasn't such a bad thing. Rumor has it, he went on to become a pretty beloved hero on his home world. Sadly, even four extra fists couldn't save him from joining the ranks of the many Spideys across the Multiverse who met their untimely demise at the hands of the Inheritors.

# PETER & BEN PARKER

## (REALITY-29320)

In a handful of realities, Peter Parker has retired from the web-swinging game and passed his webs down to his next of kin. In Reality-29320, Peter never wanted his son, Ben, to follow in his footsteps. When his exploits as Spider-Man seemingly led to the death of his wife, Mary Jane, Peter packed up his tights for good and left his days as a hero in the past.

But as much as he wanted to bury his history, his bloodline couldn't be denied. When young Ben discovered his own emerging spider-powers, he dug up his dad's old duds and brought the legend of Spider-Man back to life. Of course, doing so made Ben a target of Cadaverous, the same creep who had supposedly killed his mom all those years ago. Peter temporarily came out of retirement to help his son face down the foe who had fractured their family. When the dust settled, Mary Jane had been miraculously brought back to life—but Peter ended up paying the ultimate price to make sure that his long-lost love got a second chance to be with their son. If that's not a heroic way to go out, I don't know what is.

# SUPERIOR SPIDER-MAN

## (REALITY-616)

True story: When I was a kid, spiders used to give me the heebie-jeebies. Having these awesome spider-powers has obviously changed my perspective a bit. But while our eight-legged friends might not cause me to cringe quite as much as they used to, there are a still a few Spiders out there who will always make my skin crawl. And at the top of that list is the so-called Superior Spider-Man, Otto Octavius.

Now, I know what you're gonna ask: "Otto Octavius? Isn't he the career super-villain better known as Doctor Octopus?!" And the answer is a big "Yep!" Most people recognize the Doc Ock from Reality-616 for his robotic tentacles and ridiculous haircut, but few people ever get to see what an insane genius he really is—mostly because our Spidey always tends to foil Otto's master plans before they can succeed. But one time, Ock managed to pull off a scheme unlike any other—one that changed Spider-Man to his core.

Not long ago, Otto was dying. Like, for real. So he devised a crazy plan to swap his mind into Peter Parker's healthy body while trapping Pete's consciousness in Otto's own rapidly declining physical form. And, as nuts as it sounds, it actually worked! Otto got a new lease on life—as well as all of Pete's spider-powers—and set out to prove that he could be a better Spider-Man than his archnemesis ever was. And the big switcheroo might have stuck, if it wasn't for Otto's ego always getting in his way.

Thankfully, things eventually went back to normal. Well, normal-*ish*. Pete's mind won back control over his body, and Otto's consciousness ended up getting transferred into a hybrid clone (which still had its own spider-powers). After that, he showed up to boss us around during a few multiversal catastrophes and even kept trying to play hero on the West Coast for a bit.

The last time I saw Otto, he'd somehow reverted back to his original body and his classic villainous ways—I don't know how, but I can't say I'm surprised. I knew his hero turn couldn't last forever. But, hey, as long as it means he won't be attending any future gatherings of my fellow Spideys, Doc Ock breaking bad again is all good with me!

# THE SPIDER

## (REALITY-15)

Since there are an infinite number of realities out there, it has to be assumed that you're occasionally going to stumble across a Peter Parker who *didn't* end up becoming a hero. But the Peter Parker from Reality-15 went way beyond just "not being a hero"—he ended up becoming a total sociopath! This sinister Spidey bonded with an alien symbiote that had the same murderous tendencies as Reality-616's Carnage. Together, the pair reveled in causing pain, earning them a whopping sixty-seven consecutive life sentences in prison.

But the Spider's adventure didn't end when he got involuntarily rebranded as inmate #24739. Somehow, his bad behavior earned him a spot on a team of Multiverse-hopping heavy hitters called Weapon X. They were tasked with correcting errors across various timelines, but, as you can probably guess, they decided to conquer those time-lines instead. The Spider eventually got so out of line that he had to be put down by one of his own teammates. So, maybe Doc Ock isn't actually as bad as I thought.

# ARACHNOSAUR

## (REALITY-99476)

There were two things about the Spider-Hero from Reality-99476 that made him stand out from all the other Spidey variants I've encountered. First, he was a member of his Earth's Fantastic Five (which, if the math checks out, is one better than our Fantastic Four). Second, and most importantly: He. Was. A. Dinosaur. This prehistoric protector came from a world where reptiles, instead of mammals, had evolved into the dominant species. So, basically, he had all of the usual spider-powers that the rest of us Spider-Totems have, plus a whole bunch of natural dino-specific charac-teristics—including pointy fangs, sharp talons, and a powerful tail. While he literally fought tooth and nail when our Spider-Army first faced off against the Inheritors, this Arachnosaur, unfor-tunately, couldn't avoid extinction.

# SPIDER-MOBILE

## (REALITY-53931)

He's the Spider-Man of Reality-53931.
But he's also a sentient car.
And his real name is Peter Parkedcar.
I can't even.

# SPIDER-MA'AM

## (REALITY-3123)

I've talked about Peter Parker's Uncle Ben a lot, because, on most worlds, he was the one who taught Pete what it meant to use his powers responsibly. But I haven't given enough credit to his Aunt May, the woman who raised Peter after Ben died. You'd think that dealing with Pete's neurotic tendencies for all those years would be enough to earn anyone official "hero" status, but the Aunt Mays on most Earths are just sweet, little old ladies (and in one reality, a much younger, much more attractive lady—but I digress).

The Aunt May from Reality-3123, however, turns that trend upside down. When she got bitten by a radioactive spider instead of her nephew, this May went into full hero mode. She even recruited the rest of her family as Team Spider-Ma'am to help fight crime in her friendly neighborhood. She's equal parts amazing and adorable! Miles told me that he teamed up with her not too long ago, when an evil alternate-dimension Aunt May who had bonded with a Carnage symbiote attacked. (Yeah, my brain has trouble wrapping around that last part, too. So, let's just move on, shall we?)

# MADAME WEB

## (REALITY-616)

After Julia Carpenter was unwittingly subjected to an experimental serum made from spider venom and rare plant extracts, she gained not only powers similar to Spider-Man, but also the ability to generate a unique form of psionic webbing with her mind. How cool is that?

As Reality-616's second Spider-Woman, Julia earned her Spidey-cred by fighting in extradimensional wars and joining the Avengers—and betraying her country and moving to Canada. (To be fair, from what I've heard, she was on the right side of that one.) But that was just the first chapter of Julia's story. There was a big twist ahead that she never saw coming—which is actually kind of ironic, for reasons you'll soon understand.

See, there was this other spider-lady who called herself Madame Web. She could basically see the future, thanks to her strong connection to the Web of Life and Destiny. When that lady got killed by one of Spidey's sinister foes, she passed her precognitive powers along to Julia. Of course, these new abilities came at a cost. Julia lost her physical eyesight, but she gained the ability to see so much more.

Now, as the new Madame Web, Julia can catch glimpses of what comes next, giving her (and all of us who know her) an early-warning system when great danger is lurking on the horizon. Sometimes her cryptic visions don't make a whole lot of sense to me (and sometimes they're just not what I want to hear at that moment), but I'm still glad Julia is there to guide our little Order of the Web toward victory.

# SPIDER-MAN

## (REALITY-50101) "SPIDER-MAN INDIA"

The whole concept of the Multiverse can be a lot to handle. When you realize that there are an infinite number of versions of you out there, well, it can be hard to feel like you're all that special. (Trust me—I've been there.) My good friend Pavitr Prabhakar from Reality-50101 went through that same brand of existential crisis the first time our Spider-Army assembled. Seeing all of those Spider-Heroes in one place shook his faith and made him worry that he might not stack up to his more established counterparts.

But it was clear from the moment I met him that Pavitr was not just a random kid from outside of Mumbai who got spider-powers during a chance encounter with some old yogi. He was destined to wear the webs because he's brilliant, brave, and selfless—traits he'd prove again and again while fighting alongside his fellow Web-Warriors. And now, I think Pavitr finally sees himself the way the rest of us have always seen him. Without a doubt, this Spider-Man is the real deal!

# KWAKU ANANSI

## (REALITY-7082)

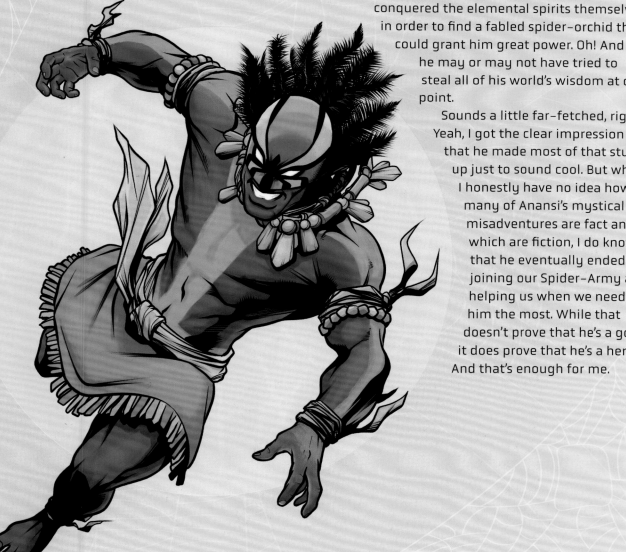

Some of the Spider-Totems out there are more than just avatars of a greater power—some are actual gods themselves. Or, at least, so they claim. Take Kwaku Anansi, a trickster and storyteller revered as a deity on the African plains of Reality-7082. According to legends (which he's more than glad to share with anyone who will listen), Anansi created the Sun, the Moon, and the stars. He also conquered the elemental spirits themselves in order to find a fabled spider-orchid that could grant him great power. Oh! And he may or may not have tried to steal all of his world's wisdom at one point.

Sounds a little far-fetched, right? Yeah, I got the clear impression that he made most of that stuff up just to sound cool. But while I honestly have no idea how many of Anansi's mystical misadventures are fact and which are fiction, I do know that he eventually ended up joining our Spider-Army and helping us when we needed him the most. While that doesn't prove that he's a god, it does prove that he's a hero. And that's enough for me.

# SPIDER-BEN & PETEY

## (REALITY-91918)

They just don't make Spider-Men any cuter than this dynamic duo from Reality-91918. I mean it! First, imagine an itsy-bitsy thirteen-year-old Peter Parker swinging around and cracking jokes. Then, imagine his rough-and-tumble Uncle Ben, who got shot by a robber and had his life saved by a transfusion of his nephew's irradiated blood. Now, they both have spider-powers and have decided to work together as a crime-fighting team! It's the perfect recipe for Spidey hijinks (which probably includes a healthy dose of valuable life lessons about power and responsibility, too, I'm guessing).

Sure, these two may have been just a couple more faces in the endless army of Spider-Heroes who helped us bring down the Inheritors once and for all, but they certainly made their mark in the short time we were together. I'm not sure what happened to them after they went back to their own reality, but if anyone deserved to have a happy ending, it was these two—am I right?

# SPIDER-MAN

## (REALITY-928) "SPIDER-MAN 2099"

The year 2099 sounds like the distant future, at least until you really stop to think about it. After all, these days, 2099 is almost exactly as far ahead of us as World War II is behind us. And since I've fought beside Captain America, it's kinda hard to ignore the fact that the future isn't as far away as it used to seem.

Anyway, in Reality-928, the future is now! And the clock isn't the only thing that took a huge leap forward in that dimension. Technology there has advanced to the point where flying cars and holographic personal assistants are the norm. Still, some things never change, and some classics never go out of style. Case in point: Miguel O'Hara, the Spider-Man of 2099.

Miguel was a brilliant geneticist working for the crazy-evil mega-conglomerate Alchemax. He got tangled up in some experiments that were way outside his ethical comfort zone and tried to quit, but his psycho boss had other plans. The dude dosed Miguel with Rapture—a super-addictive drug manufactured by Alchemax—assuming it would force Miguel to stay on board in order to get his fix. Instead, Miguel decided to use his research to reset his own DNA, but his attempt was sabotaged and his genetic code got mixed up with the DNA of—say it with me, now—a spider!

Naturally, Miguel became the Spider-Man of his era, using his new powers—including organic webbing spun directly from his wrists—to protect his world from high-tech super-villains and hostile corporations alike. He eventually found himself swinging through more than just the streets of Nueva York, traveling across dimensions and into the past to spend some quality time here in the present-day world of Reality-616.

Anyone who's ever seen a sci-fi flick knows that changing the past can wreak havoc on the future, and when Miguel eventually made his way back to 2099, things weren't quite the way he had left them. Even if the future that he knew had been rewritten, though, that didn't stop this anachronistic arachnid from trying to save it. Like I said, some things never change.

# GHOST SPIDER

## (REALITY-11638)

When I picked out the name Ghost-Spider, I thought I was being pretty original—but one thing I've learned about the Multiverse is that there's inevitably someone else who did it first. Turns out, there was already a Ghost Spider in Reality-11638. Other than the name, though, there's not much we share in common. This version of Peter Parker was from a seemingly perfect world where he was wealthy, powerful, and beloved—and, frankly, kind of a jerk. In order to stay on top, he'd use the fancy tech from the company he built, Parker Technologies, to 'port in other Spider-Heroes from alternate worlds. Then he'd siphon off their powers to strengthen himself. (Like I said, kind of a jerk.)

His plans eventually backfired and his soul got trapped in hell, but he somehow got a chance at redemption and became that dimension's Spirit of Vengeance—the Ghost Spider. Is he the ideal alternate Spidey to share a name with? Probably not. But one look at that flaming skull of his and I can guarantee one thing: I'm not about to be the one who serves him a cease-and-desist order!

# SPIDER-MAN

## (REALITY-2149)

## "ZOMBIE SPIDER-MAN"

By now, you probably have a pretty good idea of what can happen to someone when they're bitten by a spider. But how about when they're bitten by a Spider-Man? The citizens of Reality-2149's Earth found that out the hard way after their most trusted heroes were infected by a gross contagion that turned them into undead cannibals with a serious hunger for brains. (Eww.) In typical Peter Parker fashion, this world's sickening Spidey was in constant conflict with himself, but his guilt was outweighed by his insatiable appetite—at least for a while.

After devouring Galactus himself, Spidey and his fellow zombie heroes used the cosmic power they absorbed to travel the galaxy in search of other species to consume. They eventually came back to Earth decades later with plans to chow down on the last remnants of humanity. Thankfully, Spidey had a change of heart (or maybe a change of stomach) and turned against his undead allies. He cooked up a plan to destroy them—and himself—before the plague could end all life on their world and spread to other realities. So, I guess he wasn't all bad.

# SPIDER-MAN

## "CYBORG SPIDER-MAN"

You want a better Spider-Man? Why not build one? That's apparently what they did in Reality-2818. Not only was their Peter Parker part man and part spider, he was also part machine. (Actually, from what I've been told, he was *mostly* machine.) I'm honestly not sure how much of the original Peter Parker was left inside of him, what with all the high-tech weaponry that he supposedly had tucked away in his body, but I'm also not sure that it really matters. According to

those who fought alongside him, he had the same senses of humor and responsibility as any other Spidey made of flesh and irradiated blood—and that's what really counts.

I never got to meet this cyborg Spidey myself, since he was permanently taken out of service during one of the Inheritors' earliest strikes. But if his tech was really as top-of-the-line as some my fellow Web-Warriors have described it, I've got hope that this upgraded arachnid could be rebuilt some-day—maybe even better, stronger, and faster than before!

# SPIDERS-MAN

## (REALITY-11580)

Being bitten by a radioactive spider isn't a pleasant experience, but it's gotta be way better than being eaten alive by a hungry horde of them! Sadly, that's exactly what happened to the Peter Parker from Reality-11580. The poor kid was touring the cutting-edge campus of Horizon Labs when he fell into an enormous colony of irradiated arachnids that were part of an experiment in genetic alteration. Pete's physical form didn't survive the experience—but his mind somehow did, transferring into the spiders and creating a singular collective consciousness that connected and controlled them all. As if that wasn't horrifying enough already, the mass of spiders then converged into a humanlike shape and put a costume over themselves to become the Spiders-Man.

Though the individual spiders that make him up tend to stick together in their appalling anthropomorphic assemblage, Spiders-Man can send individual arachnids off to do his dirty work for him. Even when they're separated, each member of the Spiders-Man's creepy clutter stays connected to the hive mind, making them the perfect spies to spread across the city—or the Multiverse.

# SILK

## (REALITY-616)

You'd think that the odds of being bitten by an irradiated spider are, like, a gazillion to one. But on the rare occasion that a spider does get flooded with a powerful dose of radiation, you can bet that little bugger is going to bite as many people as it can before it spins its final web!

Cindy Moon, my spider-sister known as Silk, is living proof of that. Not only was she in attendance at the scientific demonstration where Reality-616's Peter Parker received his powers, she was also bitten by the exact same enhanced arachnid just a few moments after Peter was. But whereas Peter soon went on to become New York City's most famous wall-crawler, Cindy's life went down a totally different path.

Cindy's spider-powers manifested in a slightly more explosive manner than Pete's, with a powerful burst of organic webbing that made her parents panic. She was already freaked out enough when Ezekiel Sims (remember him?) showed up and told her that her status as a Spider-Totem would make her a target of the transdimensional hunter named Morlun. Not wanting to put those she loved in danger, Cindy voluntarily went into lockdown in a safe house that Ezekiel had built to protect her from Morlun and his fellow Inheritors. And that's where she stayed, completely cut off from the outside world, for the next thirteen years!

Her path would cross Peter Parker's once again when he broke Cindy free from her bunker and delivered the good news that Morlun was dead (or, at least, so he thought at the time). Taking the super-cool code name Silk, she and Spidey would quickly become close allies—way closer than either of them could've anticipated. I guess being bitten by the same spider linked them together in a way that made their Spider-Senses go absolutely crazy when they were around each other. For a while there, they could barely keep their hands off each other long enough to punch bad guys. It was gross.

Once they managed to untangle themselves from each other's webs, Silk went on to become her own hero, completely independent of Spider-Man. She's worked hard to rebuild the life she lost during all those years she spent hidden away and find her new place in the world. If you ask me, she's done a pretty sensational job of it. Silk has proven herself to be an A-list Spider-Hero right here on the streets of New York City alongside the Order of the Web as well as globally as a member of the Agents of Atlas.

# SPIDER-MAN J

## (REALITY-7041)

Some of the Spider-Heroes I've met come from realities that seem, well, a little less than real. It's almost like they were ripped straight out of a video game or a vintage Saturday-morning cartoon. That's not meant as an insult, mind you, just an observation. I mean, for all I know, every one of us is just a character in someone else's grand story.

Wow—OK, I'm getting off track here. I guess I was just trying to say that certain Spideys, like Sho Amano from Reality-7041, raise a lot of questions about what is real and what isn't. The kid looks like he sprang to life from the pages of my favorite Japanese comics. I mean, how is he completely in black and white when the rest of the world around him is in full color? Is that one of the side effects from his mystic spider-powers? I really don't know. And maybe that's for the best—because I'm not 100 percent sure my mind could handle the answer.

# SPIDER-MAN

## (REALITY-2301)

## "MANGAVERSE SPIDER-MAN"

My pal J isn't the only Spidey who seems like he'd fit perfectly into my manga collection. You know how the Peter Parkers on most worlds were taught by their Uncle Bens to be upstanding citizens? Yeah, well, the Peter Parker of Reality-2301 was trained by his Uncle Ben to be an honest-to-goodness ninja! That dimension's Ben Parker was the sensei of the legendary Spider Clan, and when he was killed, his nephew became the clan's last remaining member. Peter continued his training in secret so that he could eventually bring his uncle's murderers to justice.

For a time, he found himself bonded with a mystical amulet obtained from the rival Shadow Clan, which granted him the ability to generate organic webbing. While his connection to the amulet was eventually severed, he later learned that his natural web-spinning abilities had somehow been retained. Ninja Pete eventually decided to carry on his late uncle's legacy further by training his girlfriend, Mary Jane Watson, in the ways of the Spider Clan. I think I might have to take a trip to their little Mangaverse myself, 'cause I'm honestly not sure I can wait for the next chapter!

# THE SPIDER-MAN

## (REALITY-31411)

Dr. Aaron Aikman was a brilliant young molecular biologist at the Ikegami Medical Center and Research Institute in Reality-31411. His work in bioengineering centered on the medical application of insect venoms. He developed some sort of radical treatment that could resequence DNA and insert cloned spider genes into a human—and he tested the process on himself. (I mean, what else was he gonna do? Run proper clinical trials? Come on!)

His insane gamble paid off and he gained extraordinary spider-powers, taking to the streets as the Spider-Man. Most Spideys I've met tend to stick to the spandex, but Aikman built a sweet suit of armor that included advanced silk-spinners to shoot the webbing solution he developed, as well as catapult propulsion boots and a neuro-pulse stinger. Dude was decked out! Unfortunately, even Dr. Aikman's hyper-genius and his incredible inventions weren't enough to protect him when Morlun came hunting.

# ARACHKNIGHT

## (REALITY-616/SOUL STONE)

When someone uses the unlimited cosmic power of the Infinity Stones to alter reality, things don't always go as planned. Like, this one time, Gamora (you know, the green lady from the Guardians of the Galaxy) was having a really bad week or something, so she trapped everyone in this reality inside of a pocket universe within the Soul Stone. But the universe folded in on itself during the process, bonding the souls of its inhabitants in unexpected ways and completely rewriting their histories.

Two of the souls that ended up fusing together belonged to Peter Parker and Marc Spector. Separately, they had been Reality-616's Spider-Man and Moon Knight. But together, they became the Arachknight—a vigilante with multiple personalities and a thirst for vengeance! When the world went back to normal (as it usually does), Pete and Marc went their separate ways. But I heard a rumor from Star-Lord that this so-called Warp World was preserved within the Soul Stone—and if it was, you can bet that the Arachknight is still defending its streets!

# SCARLET SPIDER

## (REALITY-616)

It's cool that Peter Parker has a lot of spider-powered variants in alternate dimensions, but if we're being honest, the guy already has more than enough genetic duplicates right here in Reality-616. Ben Reilly may have been the first clone that Pete ever encountered, but he wasn't Miles Warren's original attempt to make a carbon copy of Spider-Man. That honor goes to the man called Kaine.

All of Warren's clones seem to suffer from a form of advanced cellular deterioration, but since Kaine was his very first attempt, his genetic structure ended up being particularly unstable. I guess an imperfect cloning process yields an imperfect clone, and Kaine has the scars—both physical and mental—to prove it. But he also got an amped-up Spider-Sense that lets him catch glimpses of the future (which is kinda cool) and a corrosive touch that can burn people's flesh (which is not so cool).

Kaine spent years going back and forth between tormenting and protecting both Pete and Ben. But when push came to shove, he stepped up and put his life on the line to defend his "brothers." After he died, Kaine was brought back to life by a multiversal Spider-being known as the Other and became its host. Their bond gave Kaine a slew of new powers for a while, and he eventually mutated into the Other's final form—a huge freaking spider—during our first big fight against the Inheritors. Kaine died again in that battle—but I guess he got better.

Last I saw him, Kaine was back to being human again. Unsurprisingly, he was still a bit unstable, but if you had gone through all the things he has, you probably would be too. The fact that he's still trying to fight the good fight as Scarlet Spider says a lot. We'll just have to wait and see how long it sticks this time.

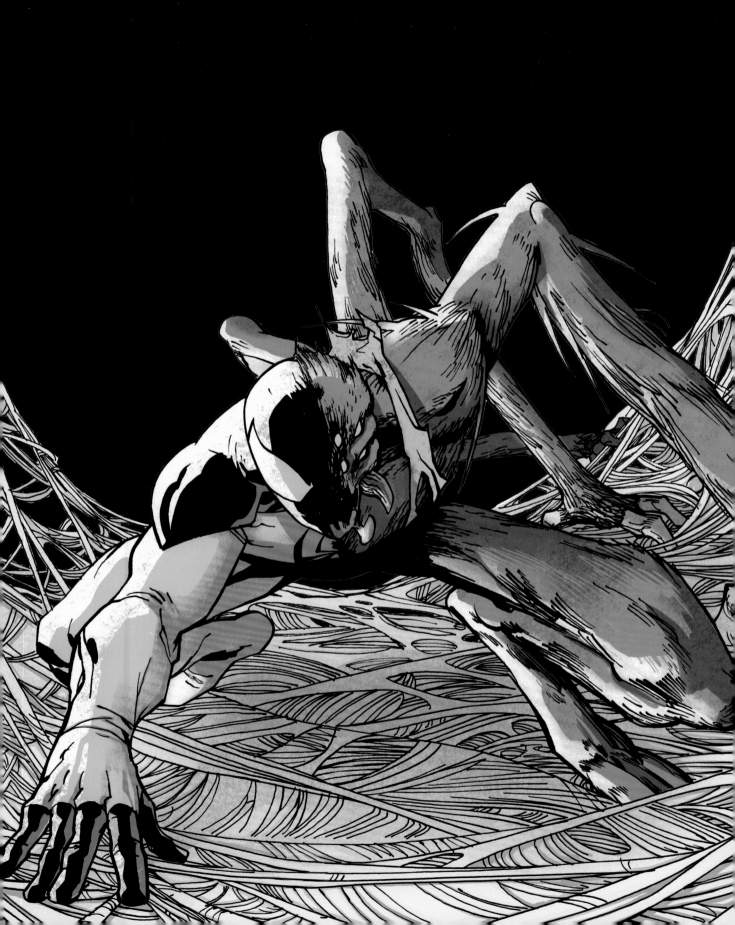

# SPIDER-MAN

## (REALITY-44145)

One thing that seems to be consistent on just about every Earth I've been to is the fact that Norman Osborn sucks. In Reality-616—and in a ton of other dimensions—he ended up becoming a nasty villain called the Green Goblin and devoted his life to tormenting Spidey. Norman's twisted schemes led to the death of Reality-616's Gwen Stacy, so I'll admit I may be a bit biased, but in my experience, even when they're given the chance to walk a better path, nine out of ten Normans find a way to turn it back toward the darkness.

The one from Reality-44145 is no exception. Even though he somehow managed to spiderify himself, all that power still wasn't enough for him. He wanted to crown himself the "savior of infinite Earths," and he was willing to destroy the Web of Life and Destiny and sacrifice the rest of his fellow Spideys to make that happen. Last I heard, Reality-616's Otto Octavius gave ol' Spider-Nor-Man the smackdown he deserved and sent him packing back to his home dimension. When someone is awful enough to make me cheer for Otto, it really says something.

# SPIDER-MAN

## (REALITY-70237)

In theory, a world without super-villains sounds kinda nice, right? It'd be a chance for us heroes to finally hang up our tights and enjoy life without all of that responsibility weighing us down. But there are always going to be new threats—sometimes from the very same people who have sworn to protect us. In Reality-70237, a group called the Reign had been appointed to lay down the law in New York City, but their merciless methods became so brutal that someone finally had to stand up to them.

That's what forced that Earth's Peter Parker to leap back into action years after he had retired his webs. Even as a really, *really* old dude, this Spidey proved that he still had some swing left in him. With a bit of unexpected help from some of his former foes, he managed to put an end to the Reign's terror and freed the people of NYC from the oppression that had been keeping them down. With a renewed sense of responsibility, old man Parker kept on going strong—until the Inheritors ended his fight once and for all.

The amazing ape-rachnid known as Spider-Monkey came from an alternate Earth where a totally different kind of primate developed into the top species. When he joined our Spider-Army against the Inheritors, this adorable little guy found a new home in our hearts. Spider-Monkey had all the powers of a spider as well as those of a monkey, and while that may seem pretty self-explanatory, it's worth pointing out because it meant that he was faster and more agile than most of us who wear the webs.

And while his cuteness factor may have been completely off the charts, that didn't mean he wasn't a ferocious fighter. In fact, back in Reality-8101, his people adhered to the laws of the animal kingdom: If any of their foes were unwilling to reform, Spider-Monkey and his fellow Ape-vengers had no qualms about removing them from the circle of life (if you know what I mean). When the Inheritors attacked us and things went totally bananas, Spider-Monkey refused to turn tail. Sadly, he was one of the many Spideys who fell at their hands.

# SPIDER-MONKEY

## (REALITY-8101)

# SPIDER-CAT
## (REALITY-999)

If you thought that last guy was too cute for words, I dare you not to swoon over this friendly neighborhood feline! Unlike Spider-Monkey, this crime-fighting kitty wasn't from a world where cats evolved into the dominant form of life. As far as I can tell, he was just a normal cat from Reality-999 who happened to have spider-powers (and what might be the sweetest little costume ever sewn). When he wasn't napping on a windowsill, I imagine he was probably busy fighting megalomaniacal mice, symbiote-bonded pigeons, or something equally adorbs.

It breaks my heart that the Inheritors put Spider-Cat down before I ever got the chance to cuddle with him. But folks always say that cats have nine lives, so I can only hope that this one had a few left to spare. After all, living on an alternate Earth can get pretty lonely sometimes. If I were ever going to take in a stray to keep me company, this domesticated defender would be the purr-fect choice!

# SPIDER-GIRL

## (REALITY-982)

My girl May Parker from Reality-982 inherited her spider-powers from her father, Peter Parker, and embraced her family legacy to become the spectacular Spider-Girl. Like her dad before her, Mayday fought to maintain that delicate balance between being a super-hero and a normal teenager. And from what she's told me, she kinda made it work—at least for a while. But any sense of normal got ripped away when the Inheritors came to her reality, murdered her dad, and tried to kidnap her baby brother, Benjy.

When I met May, she was fiercely determined to keep little Benjy from being sacrificed to fulfill one of the Inheritors' ancient prophecies. Luckily, she had me and an entire Spider-Army to back her up. With everything she had been through, it would have been so easy for May to seek revenge against the monsters who had caused her family so much pain. But all those lessons about power and responsibility must've really sunk in. When the battle reached its end, May refused to kill her enemy, choosing justice over vengeance. Her pops would've been so proud of her. I know I was.

After Benjy was safe again, May wanted nothing more than to go back to her home reality and focus on her family. But she also knew that there were lots of worlds out there that had lost their protectors because of the Inheritors. So she did the selfless thing and joined me (and some of our fellow Web-Warriors) to keep those dimensions safe. I'm glad she did, 'cause when us Spider-Girls stick together, there's nothing in any reality that can stand in our way!

# VENOM

The May Parker from Reality-9997 had a slightly different hero's journey than the Mayday I know and love. Not only did this May inherit her father's spider-powers, she also became bonded to the powerful symbiotic alien life-form known as Venom. Apparently, the symbiote thought that it could use May to get revenge on Peter for rejecting it years earlier. Fortunately, May's strong will and finely honed Spider-Sense helped her keep her new partner in check.

That didn't mean Pete was thrilled to see his daughter wearing his hand-me-down alien costume/archnemesis, though! May's new identity caused a pretty big rift between the two of them for a while, but they managed to make amends and eventually joined forces, facing countless super-powered threats on their Earth together.

# SPIDER-MAN

## (REALITY-9997)

On an Earth where everyone developed superpowers as a result of planetwide exposure to the Inhumans' Terrigen Mist, a hero like Spider-Man doesn't feel nearly as essential anymore. Or at least that's what the Peter Parker from Reality-9997 allowed himself to believe. To be fair, the guy had been through a lot—his wife had died, his secret identity had been revealed to the public, and his daughter had donned an alien costume that had tried to kill him more times than he cared to remember. It was no wonder this Pete wanted to run away from everything, including his responsibility.

Thankfully, he snapped out of his funk when his daughter was in danger, and got back into the fight. His old red-and-blues didn't fit him quite as well as they used to, so he traded them in for some NYPD blues. As an officer of the law, Pete rededicated himself to using his powers in a way that could do the most good while still making his daughter proud.

# SPIDERS MAN

## (REALITY-9997)

Not to be confused with the Spider-Man of his Earth (or the other guy from Reality-11580 who calls himself Spiders-Man), Reality-9997's Spiders Man gained his powers from the mutagenic Terrigen Mist. The red, reptilian scales he developed may resemble the pattern of a classic Spidey costume, but don't let that fool you. His other abilities are nothing like the standard set of spider-powers shared by most of our cross-dimensional counterparts.

Instead, Spiders Man is able to generate these weird energy webs that create lifelike illusions in the minds of anyone that they touch. He can make people relive the worst moments of their lives—or trap them in a fantasy world so elaborately constructed that they have no idea it isn't real. Despite his name, I'm almost certain that Spiders Man doesn't qualify as an official Spider-Totem, but it's still worth knowing that he's out there. After all, powers like his could cause some serious problems in the hands of someone on the wrong side of the battle—and for some reason, that's where Spiders Man almost always seems to be.

# THE THOUSAND

## (REALITY-616)

Carl King was a typical school bully, taking great pleasure in the pain he caused Peter Parker of Reality-616. He must've laughed pretty hard when their class went on a field trip to a science lab and "Puny Parker" got bitten by a radioactive spider. But Carl stopped laughing when he discovered that his favorite punching bag had secretly become Spider-Man.

Convinced that it should have been him who got those amazing abilities, Carl went back to the lab to search for the spider that started it all. Since the shriveled husk he found was no longer able to do any more biting, Carl did the next-best (worst?) thing and bit the spider instead—in fact, he ate the whole thing! (Totally disgusting, I know!) Soon, his insides morphed into a sentient colony of spiders, wearing Carl's skin like a suit. He devoured dozens of other innocent people over the years, living in their skins as he waited for the perfect moment to strike back at Spidey. Pete thinks he managed to exterminate this loser, but if even one of Carl's spiders survived, I worry that the Thousand could come back one day, stronger and meaner than ever.

# SPIDER-MAN

## (REALITY-90214)

### "SPIDER-MAN NOIR"

The Spider-Man from Reality-90214 reminds me of one of the characters from the old-timey detective flicks that my dad and I used to watch together late at night back when I was a kid. You know the type—a hard-boiled gumshoe who leads with his fists and calls women "dames" and "dolls." Normally, if anyone called me "doll," I'd lead with my fists too—but from this Spidey, it's almost endearing for some reason.

On his Earth, it's still the 1930s (give or take), and Peter Parker found himself wrapped up in a tangled web of crime and deception. After discovering an ancient statue of a spider god in a warehouse full of stolen antiques, Pete was bitten by one of the spiders that had stowed away in the crate. He had some crazy vision of that spider god telling him he had been chosen to serve, and, when he woke up, he was emerging from a web cocoon with nifty new powers.

The two of us became pretty tight during our first Spider-war against the Inheritors, and afterwards we kept our team-up going strong alongside our fellow Web-Warriors. So, when Pete sacrificed himself in an attempt to stop the Inheritors from returning, all of us who'd grown close to him had to live through our own version of the Great Depression. After the battle was over, I was the one who went back to his Earth and broke the news of Pete's death to his loved ones. It hurt, but it was the least I could do to honor his memory.

Just like any classic noir film, though, there was an unexpected plot twist. Miles recently went on a trip through the Multiverse and found himself mask-to-mask with our pal Pete, alive and well in his home reality. According to him, he really did die, but that spider god of his wasn't done with him yet. He woke up in another one of those weird cocoons and found himself with a fresh start. I sure am glad he did, because even though his powers may be spider based, this Peter Parker is the bee's knees!

# SPIDER-MAN, SPINNERET, & SPIDERLING

## (REALITY-18119)

"Happily ever after" isn't something that most super-heroes get, despite our seemingly unending efforts to slay every metaphorical dragon that rears its ugly head. But the Peter Parker in Reality-18119 came pretty darn close. On that Earth, he and Mary Jane Watson got married and had a daughter named Anna-May.

When Annie was a kid, she started developing spider-powers just like her dad's. In most dimensions, that wouldn't be a huge problem, but their world was ruled by a mad despot named the Regent. This guy had captured or killed nearly all of their Earth's heroes and villains so that he could siphon off their powers for himself. Peter managed to keep himself under the radar for years, but when he realized his daughter might be in danger because of the powers she'd inherited, he knew it was time to come out of the shadows.

Pete, Mary Jane, and Annie took down the Regent together, realizing in the process that this whole Spidey thing made for a surprisingly good family business. Annie embraced her natural-born abilities and became Spiderling. Meanwhile, MJ got a high-tech suit based on the Regent's designs, artificially replicating her husband's powers so that she could become Spinneret. Their amazing Spider-fam fought side by side by side to make their world a better place in the aftermath of the Regent's reign. And when we needed them to come and help us save the Spider-Verse, Pete and MJ couldn't have been prouder to see their little princess step up to take her place in the Web of Life and Destiny as its new Patternmaker.

# SPIDER-MAN

## (REALITY-8351) "SPIDER-ASSASSIN"

Most Spideys follow a simple rule: "No one dies." Not only does that mean we protect the innocent people who depend on us to watch over them, it also means we do everything in our power to find non-lethal methods to bring our adversaries to justice.

But like I said, that's just a rule followed by *most* Spideys. The Spider-Man from Reality-8351 had no interest in letting his foes walk away from a fight. Instead, he trained with Wolverine to hone his combat skills and spider-powers in order to become the perfect killing machine. He believed that great power resulted in even greater enemies, and that it was his responsibility to end their threats for good. With web-shooters retrofitted to fire bullets, he was willing to do whatever it took to finish the job. It's no wonder that this arachnid assassin was handpicked by Otto Octavius to join our Spider-Army. But even methods as ruthless as his proved to be no match for the brutality unleashed by the Inheritors.

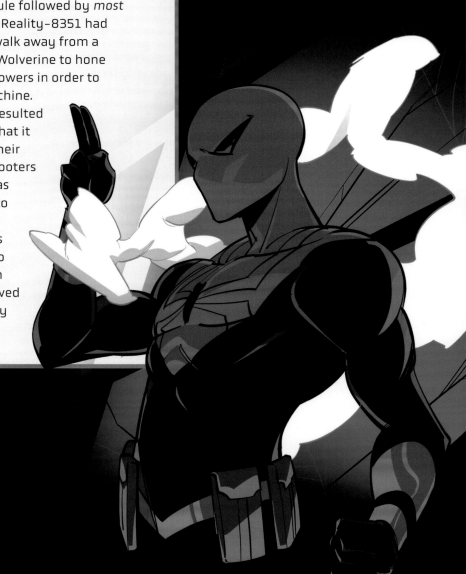

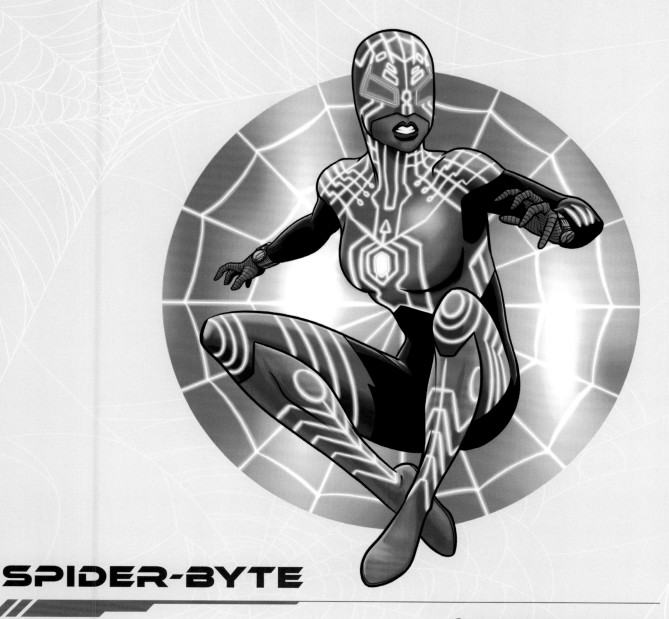

# SPIDER-BYTE

## (REALITY-22191)

I met Margo from Reality-22191 a while back when I was jumping between dimensions and recruiting every Spidey I could find for the big final battle against the Inheritors. Her Earth is one where people live out just about every aspect of their daily lives in cyberspace (which makes me feel slightly better about how much time I spend staring at my phone). Their immersive virtual landscape is like an entire reality of its own, and, just like every other reality, that means it has plenty of people eager to exploit its flaws.

That's where Margo came in. Digitally disguised as the virtual webslinger called Spider-Byte, she helped stop cybercriminals before they could steal the identities and drain the bank accounts of innocent users. I'll admit, I have zero idea where Margo found the tech required to bring her Spider-Byte persona into the physical world—but I'm certainly not going to complain that she did!

# SPIDER-HAM

## (REALITY-8311)

In the time since I first pulled on this mask, I've encountered my share of weirdness—lizard men; old guys in bird suits; rabid, weaponized koalas—you name it, I've probably punched it. So, when I first met Peter Porker—the Spectacular Spider-Ham—it's likely that I handled his level of strange better than most other folks would.

My pal Ham was born over in Reality-8311 on an Earth where everyone is a funny talking animal of some sort. You probably think you've got his origin all figured out, but ten bucks says you're wrong. See, in a twist on the classic theme, he was actually a spider who got bitten by a radioactive pig. (Yeah, you read that right.) He kept his natural spider-powers but grew to porcine proportions. I know it sounds absurd, but this is a guy who fights the Green Gobbler and Doctor Octopussycat, so, I mean . . .

It'd be fair to assume that a cartoony little pig man wouldn't be able to hold his own against a family of multiversal life-force vampires, but Spider-Ham turned out to be one of our most valuable allies in the fight against the Inheritors. Part of that is due to the fact that the basic laws of physics seem to operate very differently with him—I've seen him get flattened, peel himself off the ground, and pop right back to normal as if nothing even happened. But it mostly has to do with how much attitude is packed into that little body of his. Trust me, this pork is extra saucy!

And because I know you're wondering, yes, there is a version of me in his world. She's a penguin who calls herself Spider-Guin. And I want her to be my new best friend. 'Nuff said.

# SPIDER-MAN

## (REALITY-41252)

## "TECH-ON SPIDER-MAN"

There's no denying that Peter Parker is brilliant. Over the years, he's designed countless gadgets and high-tech costumes to help him in his fight against evil. But when it comes to building elaborate suits of cutting-edge armor, no one even comes close to the genius level of Tony Stark—aka Iron Man.

And the Tony from Reality-41252 really had to put his skills to the test after all of his fellow Avengers (including Spider-Man) were depowered by the Red Skull. Pete may not

have had his spider-powers anymore, but he wasn't about to quit the fight. Lucky for him, Tony was in a sharing mood. He built a fleet of mechanized armor suits, each one specialized to meet the needs of the individual hero wearing it. Powered by the fractured shards of the Infinity Stones, these Iron Avengers set a new standard for technology and heroism alike. As cool as I am with my current costume, I'm seriously considering swinging over to his reality to get me one of these!

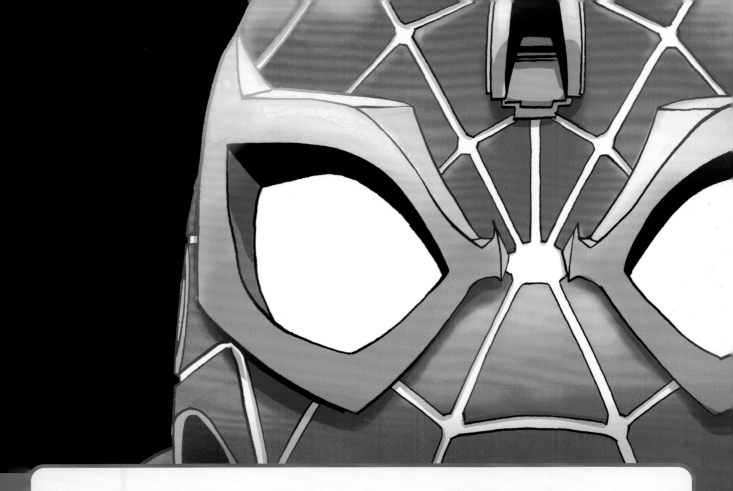

# SPIDER-MAN     (REALITY-50810)

## "MEGA MORPHS SPIDER-MAN"

The Spider-Man from Reality-50810 pilots an enormous transforming super-hero assault-bot called the Arachno-Fighter. It has an omnissum-strength core, diamond-melting hyper-lamps, and tons of other high-tech gizmos that sound totally made up to me. Apparently, on this Spidey's world, a bunch of heroes and villains have these crazy mechs—known as Mega Morphs—and use them to duke it out in the middle of major cities. (Property insurance must be a total nightmare to get there.)

Having a giant indestructible robot on our side seemed like a no-lose situation—until that same giant indestructible robot got taken over by the collective consciousness of an entire army of Electros. Not exactly the best moment for our band of Web-Warriors. We managed to turn things around, though, regaining control of the Mega Morph and using it like a super-amplifier to broadcast a powerful signal across the Web of Life and Destiny. Thanks to our massive metal friend, we saved the Multiverse with millions of volts of pure rock 'n' roll! It was sick. We ended that adventure together on a high note, but I still think I might wait a while before I start planning a reunion tour.

# SPIDER-MAN

## (REALITY-21619)

After I lost my spider-powers, I regained similar abilities by bonding with a symbiotic costume. Overall, it's been a solid relationship. (Mostly.) But my experience seems to be the exception rather than the rule. The majority of symbiotes across the Multiverse tend to bring out the worst in those who wear them. The Peter Parker of Reality-21619 was unfortunate enough to be dragged into the darkness by his symbiote's sinister side. After his Aunt May was killed, Pete gave into his alien costume's primal urges, slaying a significant chunk of his rogues gallery.

When Pete finally rejected his vicious partner, the Venom symbiote didn't take their breakup too well. It spawned a horde of offspring and attacked NYC. Pete rallied his fellow heroes to save the day, but too many lives had already been lost—including the Fantastic Four's Reed Richards. Taking responsibility for everything that went down, Pete turned himself in. (Been there, done that.) Cleared of any wrongdoing due to Venom's corruptive influence, Pete took over Reed's vacant slot on the FF as a first step on his long road to redemption.

# THE OTHER

## [ALL REALITIES]

By now, I think you understand that most Spider-Men and Spider-Women have counterparts across all dimensions. But there are a few Spider-beings that exist only at a singular point in the Multiverse. These godlike entities are deeply tied to the Web of Life and Destiny and have fancy names like the Bride, the Scion, and the Other. Each of these deities selects a single Spider-Totem from somewhere in the Multiverse to personify them. Prophecies say that the ritual sacrifice of these arachnid avatars could mean the end of all Spideys—which is one of the reasons the Inheritors were so keen on hunting them down.

A while back, the Other selected Peter Parker from Reality-616 to represent it—which seems like the obvious choice to me—but Pete rejected its power. So, it settled for Pete's clone Kaine instead. The Other expanded Kaine's range of spider-powers for a time, eventually emerging in its true giant-spider-god form to fight the Inheritors. It didn't survive the encounter, but thanks to some recent repairs to the ol' Web, there's good reason to believe that the Other hasn't chosen its last champion just yet.

# CONCLUSION

Well, there you have it—your own personal guided tour of the Spider-Verse. I know it's a lot to digest (and, frankly, I could nap for a week after all of that explaining), but hopefully you learned something useful. Chances are you won't have to rely on this knowledge to save the Multiverse anytime soon—we've got that part covered—but at least you'll know who's swinging to the rescue the next time a legion of omni-dimensional villains shows up in your neighborhood, right? Plus, if you're anything like me, you probably made a bunch of super-cool wall-crawling friends along the way.

Of course, it's also pretty clear that we've lost way too many amazing allies during our recent adventures. I won't lie—it's honestly kinda sad looking back. But in a way, I guess that's what my whole class project was all about in the first place, right? If we take the time to learn more about those who came before us, it helps us cling to their memories and walk the webs in ways that would've made them proud.

And don't panic—there are more Spideys still swinging than I could possibly count. It's a big Multiverse, after all, and we've barely even begun to scratch the surface. I mean, we didn't even get to that version of Black Cat who donned the webs to become Night-Spider. Or the very *unfriendly* neighborhood Spider-Hulk. Oh, and don't forget the Spidey with the unhealthy obsession with those little cream-filled sponge cakes! And those are just a few of the official Spider-Men and Spider-Women out there. You wouldn't believe how many other weird variations of me I've run across! (Seriously: There's a Captain Gwen-Merica—I kid you not.)

Yeah, I could probably fill, like, ten more of these notebooks with all of the crazy stuff I've seen. But that's gonna have to wait for another time. My Spider-Sense is telling me I'm late for class—gotta swing!

—Gwen

# FURTHER READING:

## MARVEL'S MOST ARACHNO-TASTIC TALES FROM THE SPIDER-VERSE

**SPIDER-MAN: THE OTHER (2005)**
*Friendly Neighborhood Spider-Man #1–4*
*Marvel Knights Spider-Man #19–22*
*The Amazing Spider-Man #525–528*

**SPIDER-MEN (2012)**
*Spider-Men #1–5*

**SPIDER-VERSE (2014)**
*Superior Spider-Man #32–33*
*Edge of Spider-Verse #1–5*
*The Amazing Spider-Man #7–15*
*Spider-Verse Team-Up #1–3*
*Spider-Verse #1–2*
*Spider-Woman #1–4*
*Scarlet Spiders #1–3*
*Spider-Man 2099 #5–8*

**SPIDER-VERSE (2015)**
*Spider-Verse #1–5*

**WEB-WARRIORS: PROTECTORS OF THE SPIDER-VERSE (2015)**
*Web Warriors #1–11*

**SPIDER-MEN II (2017)**
*Spider-Men II #1–5*

**SPIDER-GEDDON (2018)**
*Edge of Spider-Geddon #1–4*
*The Superior Octopus #1*
*Spider-Geddon #0–5*
*Peter Parker: The Spectacular Spider-Man #311–313*
*Spider-Gwen: Ghost-Spider #1–4*
*Spider-Girls #1–3*
*Spider-Force #1–3*
*Vault of Spiders #1–2*

**SPIDER-VERSE (2019)**
*Spider-Verse #1–6*

Published by Titan Books, London, in 2023.

# TITAN
## BOOKS

A division of Titan Publishing Group Ltd
144 Southwark Street
London SE1 0UP
**www.titanbooks.com**

Find us on Facebook: www.facebook.com/titanbooks
Follow us on Twitter: @TitanBooks

Published by arrangement with Insight Editions, San Rafael, California.
www.insighteditions.com

A CIP catalogue record for this title is available from the British Library.

ISBN: 9781803365978

Publisher: Raoul Goff
VP of Licensing and Partnerships: Vanessa Lopez
VP of Creative: Chrissy Kwasnik
VP of Manufacturing: Alix Nicholaeff
VP, Editorial Director: Vicki Jaeger
Managing Editor: Maria Spano
Designer: Amy DeGrote and Lola Villanueva
Editor: Scott Nybakken
Editorial Assistant: Harrison Tunggal
Senior Production Editor: Elaine Ou
Senior Production Manager: Greg Steffen
Senior Production Manager, Subsidiary Rights: Lina s Palma-Temena

ROOTS OF PEACE          REPLANTED PAPER

Insight Editions, in association with Roots of Peace, will plant two trees for each tree used in the manufacturing of this book. Roots of Peace is an internationally renowned humanitarian organization dedicated to eradicating land mines worldwide and converting war-torn lands into productive farms and wildlife habitats. Roots of Peace will plant two million fruit and nut trees in Afghanistan and provide farmers there with the skills and support necessary for sustainable land use.

Manufactured in China by Insight Editions

10 9 8 7 6 5 4 3 2 1